Me and My Sparrow

Yvonne Valle

Illustrated by Grace Vanderbush

DIVINE PURPOSE
Publishing
KIDS

Me and My Sparrow was inspired in the summer of 1964
while author Yvonne Valle was living in New York City.
One morning, a bird really fell from his nest and into her life.
The author hopes you enjoy this true story.

In a high-rise apartment in New York City,
there lived a young girl named Eve.

Right above her window,
there was a baby sparrow in his nest.

Eve could always hear the baby sparrow
chirping in the early mornings.

One day, the sparrow fell out of its nest
and right into her room.

Eve called her daddy
to tell him what had happened.

They could not reach the nest to return the sparrow.
The bird had also injured his claw.

So, her daddy decided that they would nurture
the sparrow back to health.

Eve and her daddy took care of the sparrow
as best as they knew how.

They made him a soft bed
of cloth inside of a milk carton.

And they fed him bread soaked in milk
three times a day so he would grow big and strong.

Months went by, and the sparrow
was feeling much better.

He was not in a cage,
so he was free to fly around the house.

In fact, the sparrow was feeling so much better
that he decided he would fly out of
the kitchen window!

Eve screamed and called
for the sparrow,
but it was no use.

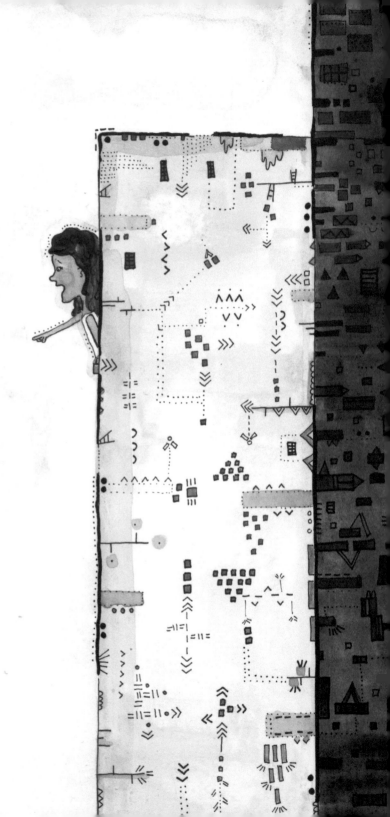

He flew across the street to another building. But that building was home to a flock of pigeons.

Soon the sparrow found himself surrounded by the pigeons who were much bigger than he was.

They began poking and hurting the sparrow. Eve yelled and tried to scare the pigeons away, but they were too far away to hear her.

Much to Eve's surprise, the sparrow played dead
so the pigeons would leave him alone.
And they did just that!

As soon as they flew away,
the sparrow got up and flew back
to Eve's window. He was safe!

The sparrow had quickly learned that he was not
yet ready to be out on his own.

Several more months passed,
and the sparrow stayed close to home.

Until one morning, Eve awoke and discovered
that the sparrow had left again!
She wondered where he had gone.
Eve was heartbroken and afraid for him.

Weeks passed but there was no sign
of the sparrow. Eve waited by her window
every day hoping that he would return.
But eventually, she gave up.

She prayed for the little bird's safety and was grateful that she could help him for as long as she did.

Then one afternoon, Eve and her parents
were getting ready to sit down and have dessert.

Eve's mommy had just served her daddy
some coffee when she screamed!

Her mommy screamed so loud
that her daddy spilled his coffee all over his lap!

The sparrow was back!

He flew all around the kitchen
and over everyone's heads until
he finally landed on her daddy's shoulder.

It was as if the sparrow came back to say
"thank you" and "goodbye."

But the sparrow didn't return alone.

A female sparrow was waiting for him

by the window sill.

He chirped all around the house.

It was the only way he could show his gratitude

for all Eve and her parents had done to help him.

The sparrow then flew out of the window,

and his female sparrow followed.

Eve and her parents never saw the sparrow again.

THE END!

Look at the birds. They don't plant or harvest or store food in barns, for your heavenly Father feeds them. And aren't you far more valuable to him than they are?

Matthew 6:26 NLT

CPSIA information can be obtained
at www.ICGtesting.com
Printed in the USA
LVHW07n2154310818
588849LV00002B/8/P